IF YOU PRAISE A WORD, IT TURNS INTO A POEM

IF YOU PRAISE A WORD, IT TURNS INTO A POEM

Selected Works From the COMPAS
Writers & Artists in the Schools Program

Edited by
Dana Jensen

Illustrations by
Marcia McEachron

COMPAS
Writers & Artists in the Schools
1992

Publication of this book is generously supported by the Sven and C. Emil Berglund Foundation, dedicated in memory of C. Emil Berglund.

COMPAS programs are made possible in part by grants provided by the Minnesota State Arts Board, through an appropriation by the Minnesota State Legislature. In the past year, the COMPAS Writers & Artists in the Schools program has received generous support from the Hugh J. Andersen Foundation, the Ashland Oil Foundation, the Cargill Foundation, the International Multifoods Charitable Foundation, Land O'Lakes and U S WEST Communications.

As always, we are grateful for the hundreds of excellent teachers throughout Minnesota who sponsor COMPAS Writers & Artists in the Schools residencies. Without their support and hard work, the writers and artists would not weave their magic, and the student work we celebrate in this book would not spring to life.

For their work in producing this book, special thanks are due to Jo Svendsen, WAITS Program Associate; to Carol Bergelund, COMPAS Office Manager; and to Daniel Gabriel, WAITS Program Director.

ISBN 0-927663-19-8

COMPAS
305 Landmark Center
75 West Fifth Street
St. Paul, Minnesota 55102

Molly LaBerge, Executive Director
Daniel Gabriel, Director, Writers & Artists in the Schools

TABLE OF CONTENTS

III. No Snowflake is the Same and This One Has Melted

IV. HE WAS JUST SHOWING HIM WHERE THE GREEN GRASS WAS

V. SURROUNDED BY EVERYTHING THOUGH NOTHING IS THERE

INTRODUCTION

If pressed for a job description of my work as a poet with the COMPAS Writers & Artists in the Schools program, the title of this anthology would work perfectly. "If you praise a word, it turns into a poem" seems to me to wonderfully capture the essence of the artistic values that COMPAS writers attempt to communicate to each student in every school we visit. As evidenced by this collection, that goal is realized and surpassed in classrooms throughout the state with remarkable frequency. Not a complex process actually, as writers share with children and young people their own love of language through favorite pieces of writing, equipping students with some of the techniques and skills, such as image, metaphor, narrative and dialogue, needed to write effectively, then setting them free to explore through words their lives, feelings and imaginations. From there the students' innate or intuitive sensibilities for creative writing take over and most often the works they produce are charged with the beauty and wonder of expressive language, where sound and meaning merge, where the music of words portrays the depth of emotion and experience of even the youngest writers.

As I assembled this anthology, selecting one piece of writing from five pieces submitted from each school that had a COMPAS writing residency this past year, I was struck over and over again by the breadth of awareness with which students perceive themselves, their lives, families and cultures. I was moved by their descriptions of past experiences, both joyous and sorrowful, that continue to resonate through their lives and into their poems, stories, songs and dramatic sketches. I was delighted and saddened by the numerous pieces about grandparents, in which students explore the pleasures of spending time together, sharing in the memories and wisdom of their elders, as well as confronting the pain and fear of seeing loved ones age and pass on. I was heartened by the students' genuine love of nature and abiding concern for animals, and their anger at our human tendencies to abuse and ravage our natural world. I was impressed by the energy and force with which students wrote about the mysteries, ambiguities and shadows of human existence, garnering unto themselves the transcendent symbols from nature, memory and experience that all writers use to establish themselves as a living presence on the written page.

That challenging, exhilarating and at times difficult process of praising words into works of art is revealed here in this book, for all of us to partake. Here, we as writers and artists, teachers and parents are given back to generously by these young people who offer to us the best of themselves through their poems, stories, dramatic sketches and, for the first time in a COMPAS anthology, songs as well. I would like to offer appreciation to Marcia McEachron for her excellent cover art and illustrations that reflect and reinforce the power and grace of the students' words. With gratitude also to all at COMPAS and in the schools throughout Minnesota who work so hard to make the Writers & Artists in the Schools program flourish, this book is offered as a gift to share among ourselves. Please read, please listen and enjoy.

Dana Jensen
July, 1992

HERE I COME. I AM THE MAGICAL HORSE.

Here I come. I am the magical horse.
I will spread my wings and glide
through the sky filled with roses. I
will glide through the clouds
and let the wind fill my
wings. I will lie on
clovers. I will find
myself running and
then galloping. The
sun will go
down and
the darkness
will
creep
up right
behind me
and all at once it
will flash. It will be
dark. When it is pitch
dark, I will see eyes in the
bushes. I will run and run wishing
the day will be right around the corner. I
will drink the cool frosty spring water. I
will eat the sweet taste of the buttercup. The
yellow of their sweet petals will make me heat up like the
sun. It will make me tired and fall asleep in a high breeze.

Kerrie Stoermann :: Grade 4
Holdingford Elementary School :: Holdingford

The Mother, The Child, The Godmother's Dream

I am the mother of the stars
that shine around the moon.
I am the child that lives in
the Big Dipper who watches
for falling stars. I am the aunt
who turns into a bat who
scares the cheetahs. I am a godmother
that comes to you every night. I am the
ancestor that is your big whales.

Andrea Nelson :: Grade 1
Aquila Primary Center :: St. Louis Park

MORNING

I am a patch of grass waving at the sun
    as it peeks overhead.
I am the sunbeams painting
    the waving grass red.
I am the dew that covers the red waving grass.
I am a tree in the waving grass that's red
    with dew all around it.
I am the leaves on the tree in the waving grass
    that's red with dew on it.
I am the things in the world that nobody sees
    in the wind's slight breeze.

Peter Denery :: Grade 5
Newport Elementary School :: Newport

If I am a thought in the wind
    My friend is a dream that is kept forever
    If I am a dancer that remains in the
circle until the world is forgotten
    My mother is a heart that will love until the end of
time
    If I am an eagle that soars through the sky like
a plane
    My grandmother is a north star that stands alone for
eternity
    If I am a timberwolf that sits alone in the midnight
wind
    My grandfather is a cheetah that runs to the beat of the
drum
    If I am an eagle that flies around the circle
    My teacher is a diamond that leads me in the right direction to a
good education
    If I am a wounded panther that is recovering from an
injured knee
    My father is a miracle that cures it for me
    If I am a bear eating berries from a tree
    My brothers are deer in the valley waiting for the
setting sun
    If I am a war pony going out for battle
    My sister is a unicorn watching me go out

Sherona Williams :: Grade 5
Blackduck Elementary School :: Blackduck

I have talked to every type of animal that lives in the forest.
I have murmured to every fish in the deep, sparkling sea.
I have echoed my voice off red, sandstone canyons.
I have whispered into the wind, my voice carried off through eternity
to some unknown place.
I've strolled through my very being, I stumbled over my past.
I've crept over my very soul.
My heart beats wildly as I hear a wolf howl into the wind.
The mighty black bear roams the forest as if all he sees is his.
I have seen ants multiply over an open candy bar.
I have seen the amount of evil done in the Amazon.
I've seen dragonflies glide through eternity, swiftly buzzing their magic
song.
I have seen Indians divided from whites like great numbers of dust
floating through space.
I have gazed through cold, arctic waters to watch the graceful whales
and seals diving deep into icy depths.
I have stared at cars crossing highways, spewing great amounts of foul-
smelling exhaust into the air.
I have pumped my living soul into a gushing creek.
I have jumped onto sandy shores.
I have loped through moss green forest.

Kelly Thompson :: Grade 5
Eisenhower Elementary School :: Hopkins

There is this stream
I cannot cross
though it is small.
It is a stream of trouble and fear
although it is happy sometimes.
It has banks of fear and anger
that nobody can divert
and change its course.
I'm the only one who can change it.
The stream is like a river that never ends
and disappears over the hill.
When I get older it will drain away.

Danny Headley :: Grade 5
Meadowbrook Elementary School :: Hopkins

LIFE STORY

When I was young and
it was evening my eyes
would be searching for
comfort. I would look
up and I would see a dog
searching through the stars
to find his master, and I saw
comets burning though the
stars with the force of
the rising sun. I would
look down and see the deer
becoming words as they fill
my heart with joy.
And I took my
friends where the water
turned to sand and
trees climbed up mountains
and people as old
as dinosaurs and people
as young as new seed–
lings are together.
We saw sharks searching for
food in the deep water
and our hunger was as
dark as the sky
at night.
We saw where clear water falls
from the sky and people cheer
about everything.

Garrett Bayrd :: Grade 5
Gatewood Elementary School :: Hopkins

I Am the Dark

I am the water inside a waterbed,
the empty space inside a bouncing ball,
the black fur on a witch's cat. I lurk behind you on your way
through the dark forest.
I am the feathers of a crow.
You may never know where I am,
but I am always near.
I surround the seeds inside an apple.
I travel through the ground,
weaving my way through roots of trees.
I am waiting in the orange,
released when the rind is peeled off.
I am inside a raindrop
created in the clouds
before a huge thunderstorm.
Then the lightning flashes
and I am forced out.

Jessica Heitman :: Grade 8
Oltman Junior High School :: St. Paul Park

My Secrets and Everything Else in the World

I know things that only my shoe's squeak knows.
I know things that only Jupiter's red eye knows.
My secrets hide in the center of the sun waiting
to burst out with flames.
My secrets move through the ground when the
farmer plants his foot in the ground's delicious
dirt. My secrets are as strong as the crashes of
two guns' bursts. My secrets are as old as the dog's
first bow wow. I know things that only the first
dinosaur knows. My secrets are as poor as a fish without
fins. My secrets are as poor as a gardener without a
garden. My voice is as old as the first star. My
secrets are as silent as a burglar stalking your
house at midnight. My secrets are as poor as a sun
without light. My secrets are as strong as the
tornado sucks thoughts.

Steven Yang :: Grade 4
Pine Hill Elementary School :: Cottage Grove

MY SECRET

My secret is like a dog
barking at my window.
My secret hides in the
desert. My secret is quiet
as my breath. My secret
moves as I live. My secret
is my guide as I live.
My secret is the shade
of me. My secret of all
is my friend. My secret
is the world. My secret
is the one. My secret
moves inside me. My
secret is my mom gliding
through the wind. My secret
is the friend.

Dana Henderson :: Grade 2
Pilot Knob Elementary School :: Eagan

MY THOUGHTS

My thoughts are like a
frog jumping from one lily pad
to the next.
My thoughts move like a
slow ballerina.
My thoughts are as old as
me.
My thoughts hide like a rabbit
in a hole.
When my thoughts pick up ideas
it is like the wind picking up
leaves.
My thoughts follow me like my
shadow does.

Michelle Peterson :: Grade 4
Swanville Public School :: Swanville

SECRET WISH

The bear cub scratches inside
     yearning to leap out.

The beaver gnaws inside
     wanting to waddle out.

The little bunny nibbles inside
     needing to hop out.

The baby wiggles inside
     neglecting to crawl out.

The childhood in all of us
     is always wishing to show.

Rachael Rudeen :: Grade 8
Oltman Junior High School :: St. Paul Park

BIKE RIDE

Childhood was like
my first bike ride—
People helped me at first,
now I am riding on my own,
riding my way
to adulthood.

I have no map,
many choices,
and no plan.
Everything is changing,
I am riding on the edge.

I first rode on grass,
now on pavement.
There are more choices
to make, things
are tougher now.
I am riding faster, faster,
and now I am at warp speed,
heading straight
into a brick wall.

Jimmy Fanjoy :: Grade 5
Lakeview Elementary School :: Robbinsdale

The Closet Monster

I am the closet monster.
I'm the big blue man
that scares the little boys
and girls right out of their pants.
At nine o'clock it's time for work.
Here I go to scare the squirt.
Finally I arrive at Tommy
Twinkle's house.
I beat my drum "bing bong, ding dong."
He's screaming and screaming,
but I'm laughing and laughing.
Tommy Twinkle's mom comes in.
"Uh oh."
She tells him that I'm just a
figure of his imagination.
Pooph I'm gone.

Sara Johnson :: *Grade 5*
Elm Creek School :: *Maple Grove*

LAUGHTER

I like to laugh at you,
You like to laugh at me.
I like to laugh at you
More than you like to laugh at me.
You cry when I laugh at you.
But when you laugh at me,
I laugh at you,
And when you laugh at me
And I don't laugh at you,
I laugh with you.

Jenny Fussy :: Grade 2
Lakeview Elementary School :: Robbinsdale

You

You, my friend, are like the earth.
Your crust so forbidding,
there is though a mystique to you
that makes me want to dig deeper.
I get through to your mantle.
There it's like another world,
not so tough,
not so hard.
There is something about it
that makes me want to find
your heart.
I know I want to find this place,
this core of you.

Mike Aschenbrener :: Grade 7
Oltman Junior High School :: St. Paul Park

OUR SUMMER VACATION

The way I was standing by my friend
outside at 8:00 getting our pictures taken,
the way bacon was sizzling on the gas stove,
the way we were in our pajamas,
the way we did not want our pictures taken
in our pajamas, the way we were shy,
the way our faces turned red as apples,
the way the sun was shining, the way
the birds were singing, the way the trees
were green, the way the sand was hot,
the way the water was splashing against
the sand, the way the toast was
crunchy, the way the wind blows.

Brian Thompson :: Grade 4
Pullman Elementary School :: St. Paul Park

HAWK

I hear the sound of a hawk.
I feel alone.
I feel like catapulting off a cliff,
opening my orange and black wings,
gliding on a thick sheet of wind
that blows through my razor sharp wings.

Ripping vertically down, changing
the angle of my wings upward,
higher and higher,
inhaling the scent of fresh soil,
seeing trees fly by, knowing

I can fly.

Eric Donald Oscarson :: Grade 6
Pinewood Elementary School :: Rochester

A Breathtaking Moment

Squished, engulfed in flesh;

pushed through, not wanting
to leave the warm tenderness.

You see a tiny opening;
your puffed legs are shocked.

Now your stomach;
you're crying, wanting to go back.

All of a sudden
you're out into air;
your body hurts.

A pair of wide-eyed owls crying,
stare at you.
You are warm in an arm of cotton.

Carrie Meissner :: Grade 7
Oltman Junior High School :: St. Paul Park

SHE POURS THE FIRE

My mother dances with flames.
She pours the fire into the dragon's mouth.
My mom cleans the utensils of God,
polishing the angels' halos.
My mom collects stars and puts them
in my dreams. She cooks
for the man in the moon.
But sometimes she is a hurricane blowing me
into a deep, dark hole.

Steve Hain :: Grade 6
Holmes Elementary School :: Rochester

Once there were two women
Who never knew each other;
One I do not remember,
The other I call mother.

One gave me a nationality,
The other gave me a name.
One gave me the seed of talent;
The other gave me an aim.

Two different lives
shaped to make mine one;
One became my guiding star,
The other became my sun.

One gave me emotions;
The other calmed my fears;
One saw my first smile,
The other dried my tears.
The first gave me life and
The second taught me to live it;
The first gave me a need for love,
And the second was there to give it.

One gave me up.
It was all she could do;
The other prayed for a child,
and God led me straight to you.

Cherie Mauricio :: Grade 10
Mahtomedi High School :: Mahtomedi

UNTITLED

I remember when I was in 6th grade the craze was Cabbage Patch kids. When Christmas came around, everybody wanted one. If you could get one it was another story. My mom happened to be one of the lucky ones. But, she only got one. And there are two of us in the family. Both of us are girls, obviously not making the decision any easier. I can almost picture my mom lying awake in her bed trying to decide who should get it.

Christmas Eve came and it was time to open presents. You get that funny feeling in the pit of your stomach. Will I get what I really want this year? I tore the paper off my biggest present under the tree. Staring out at me from the cellophane were two tiny green Cabbage Patch eyes. She was mine! I took her out of the box and she smelled wonderful. I looked over to my sister to see if she had gotten one, too. She hadn't. Instead, my mom had spent many late night hours making a doll for her. She had a hand-painted face and curly brown hair that my mom had spent hours curling around a pencil and tying with string. I thought she was just as cute as mine. My sister didn't think so. She threw the doll on the floor and shouted, "I hate it—how come Stacie got the real one? I hate it."

I couldn't believe what she said after my mom put so much work into that doll. All I remember thinking was, "What a little brat!"

My mom had a hurt expression on her face and quickly went to the bathroom. My dad sent my sister in there to try and make things better. I got an idea to fix this Christmas yet. I walked in the bathroom and threw the Cabbage Patch at my sister and told her to keep it. When I was walking out, I heard my mother crying. It was the first time I had ever heard my mother cry and it was awful. You always expect her to be the strong one.

It really was a terrible Christmas. I hope when my sister looks back on that, she is truly embarrassed. It made me realize how much love goes into a handmade gift. It also made me realize how much my mother loves us and that she has feelings too.

Stacie Lee :: Grade 12
Roseau High School :: Roseau

The picture I see looks so happy
yet I don't know why.
This is the saddest place to be.
He lays there so limp, he looks so sad,
yet there's a smile on his face.
He'd give all he has for just one more
step. For he will never walk again.
He will never run. To him, his life
is over. No more will he dream. No more
will he want a car, a house,
no more money, riches, gold.
All he wants is one more chance
to bring back the past.

This day still remembered
 in his mind; the terrifying moment
replays all day and night.

He thinks his life is over.
If only he could leave
this world, just to be alone.
One more chance is all he has
to have the world at his mercy.

The broken branch still
on the ground—the culprit,
though not human, still laying
on the ground as if waiting.

Waiting for him to return,
the only way to be free, free of terror,
free at last to live a life
of happiness, to live a life
of glee. To leave the past

and let it lie beneath
the old broken tree.

Erica Schatzlein :: Grade 5
Oak Grove Intermediate School :: Bloomington

A DARKENING NIGHTMARE

I sat down to the comfort of my young,
    vibrant and childish body,
only to face the darkening nightmare of
    divorce.
There was the absent look on their faces.
All my smiling glory was swept away.
It was so cold and distressed I only felt
    the warmth of my little bear as I hugged it
    close,
There came the soft sweep of a nervous hand
    across the table as my mother spoke.
The terrible words she announced came across
    like the sharp cries of a baby.
They took frequent and frightening stabs at
    my heart,
devouring it bit by bit.
All the fears and worries of life fled
    into my young body,
too young to carry the load.
Charging through, they pushed away all the
    laughter and happiness I had ever known
    and had,
making my body empty.
It was an emptiness that never would go
    away.
It was then I realized all the life I had
    ahead of me,
and all the changes and experiences to come
    with it.

Alison Brueggemann :: Grade 7
Blake Middle School :: Hopkins

THE SIZE OF A GRAPE

Anh Tai Luc is a name
    that belongs to my brother.
Knives, guns, death and war are
    a part of his name.

A demon lived in his mother's womb.
It attacked him as a fetus,
    and left him scarred for life.
Three fingers on one hand,
    four on the other.
A hole in his heart
    the size of a grape.
Surgery after surgery will never
    make him normal.

His arrival on the plane from Vietnam
    to America was a joyous occasion
    for me and my family.
For him, a new and vulnerable transition.
An ocean of tears, a lifetime
    of racism,
the death of every possible
    show of dignity.

Jen Fulton :: Grade 11
Alternative Learning Center :: St. Paul Park

Song from "The Prince of Tides"

My parents were constantly in war
Against each other.
It was a constant
Never-ending terror.
We had a place,
A special place,
Where we all were in total peace.

All three of us would plunge
Into the lake.
At the bottom, we would join
Hands with our eyes open
Under the water
In our clothes.

We stayed there until our lungs
Ran out.
We then would lie on the deck
to dry off
So Mother would not
Beat us too.

Marianne Beare :: Grade 5
Voyager School :: Moorhead

To Parents

You are like a beacon pointing the way
on a cloudy day.

You are like a wave in a stormy ocean
when I disagree with you.

When you're angry, you fill my life
with misery.

When you're cheerful on Monday mornings,
you depress me.

When you're angry with me, I feel as small
as a grain of sand on a huge shore.

When I'm sick, you stick by my side,
even though I may spew on you.

I am really glad you're my parents,
because if it weren't for you,
I'd be broke.

Manya Twite :: Grade 6
Dodge Center Elementary School :: Dodge Center

Scene: The hot, hot desert. The BOY enters, crawling. Sound of drums beating. Someone with a cut-out of the SUN follows him, sizzling and hissing and shining heat down on the BOY.

> BOY
> (Crawling)
Water. . . . Water. . . . Pepsi!. . . .

> (He collapses.)

> MUSIC: A flute playing sweetly. The SAND WHALE enters. The SAND WHALE is made up of six people playing the spout. They wave colorful streamers to indicate that the WHALE flies. The WHALE stops by the BOY.

> WHALE
Come with me.

> BOY
Well . . . um . . . Okay . . .

> The BOY gets on the WHALE. They fly.

> BOY
I'm Flying!! Whee! Whee! I'm Flying!

> The WHALE takes the BOY to a Pepsi machine, and gives the BOY money.

> BOY
Thank you.

> The WHALE flies off. The BOY puts money in the machine, which is played by three people. They each make clanky machine noises, and the Pepsi can clunks out. The BOY opens the Pepsi, drinks and is refreshed.

> BOY
Ahhhhhhh. . . .

Scene change.

The parents are at home. DAD is pacing. MOM is trying to soothe DAD.

DAD
Where is he?

MOM
He'll be all right, dear.

DAD
Where is he?

MOM
He'll be all right, dear.

DAD
Where is he?

MOM
He'll be all right, dear.

DAD
Where is he?

MOM
He'll be all right, dear.

The BOY enters the house. DAD and MOM yell at him.

DAD
Son, where were you?

MOM
WE WERE WORRIED ABOUT YOU.

BOY
These flying whales picked me up in the desert—

DAD
SON, WHERE WERE YOU?

MOM
WE WERE WORRIED ABOUT YOU.

BOY
I'm trying to tell you, these whales picked me up and we flew—

DAD
SON, WHERE WERE YOU?

MOM
WE WERE WORRIED ABOUT YOU.

BOY
FLYING . . . THESE WHALES . . . FLYING . . .

DAD
SON, WHERE WERE YOU?

MOM
WE WERE WORRIED ABOUT YOU.

BOY
FLYING . . . THESE WHALES . . . FLYING . . .

DAD
ENOUGH!! You're grounded for a week. Go to your room.

The BOY looks at his MOM. She nods her head. He walks
dejectedly off stage.

BOY
Why don't they ever believe me?

He slams the door behind him. Huge drum beat to make the
sound of the door slamming.

Scene change

The boy in his room. He stares at the Pepsi can.

BOY
What about the whales? Why don't they ever believe me? What about
the whales . . . ? Why don't they ever believe me . . . ?

He falls asleep. Dream Music begins: wind chimes and guitar.
Four people circle around the BOY: two people with musical

instruments that sound like ticking clocks, one person carrying a "Sun" and one person carrying a "Moon." They circle around him and chant:

TIME PEOPLE
Sunday. Monday. Tuesday. Wednesday. Thursday. Friday. Saturday. Sunday.

The TIME PEOPLE exit. The BOY wakes up.

BOY
I have to find the Whales.

He exits through the door of the house.

Scene Change.

The BOY is in the desert, at the Pepsi machine. He buys a Pepsi and sticks it in his pocket. He walks around the stage, calling out:

BOY
Whales . . . Whales! . . . Whales!!

The HAPPY SAND WHALE enters, flying, with flute music.

WHALE
Happy to see you again.

The BOY gets on the WHALE, flies off.

The MAILMAN enters, crosses to the Whale kingdom where the BOY is now.

MAILMAN
Any mail to deliver?

BOY
Take this letter to my Mom and Dad.

MAILMAN exits, whistling, with the letter.

Scene Change

Back to the House. DAD is pacing like before.

DAD

I can't believe he ran away. I can't believe he ran away.

MOM

He'll be all right, dear.

MAILMAN knocks on the door. Drum strikes make the sound of
his knocking. MOM opens the door, gets the letter. MAILMAN
exits. MOM reads the letter, soft music under.

MOM

"Dear Mom and Dad. I flew off with the whales."

DAD

WHAT?

MOM

Shhh. "I'll come back. Maybe in two years. I might not come back."

DAD

I don't believe it! He's hiding in the desert. Let's go find him.

They go out into the desert. Scene Change. They walk around
the stage in large circles. The person with the cut-out of the SUN
follows them, sizzling and hissing at them. They grow hot and
tired, until they collapse in the desert. The SAND WHALE
enters, flying, with the BOY riding it. The WHALE stops near
the parents, who look up amazed. The BOY dismounts, helps the
PARENTS up, and offers them the Pepsi in his pocket. They
drink it and are refreshed. They all get on the whale, and while
flute music plays, fly off to the Whale Kingdom. The BOY,
MOM and DAD dismount, and they dance in a circle holding
hands and smiling, while the flute plays and they do a dance.

THE END

Josiah Larson :: Grade 4
J. F. Kennedy Elementary School :: Hastings

THE BROTHERS

I stand with a click
goes the camera in my front
yard with the tree like
the moon with my stupid
brother with wormy arms
my hair like a tidal wave
the rose-red tulips like
light bulbs I have lazer
shorts on. While the
picture is taken my
brother calls me dumbbell
so I say, runs through
the family, and he
walks away and
I think I love
it when I
win.

Isaac Foreman :: Grade 3
Cedar Manor Elementary School :: St. Louis Park

FEATHER LIGHT

My sister crashes through the squeaky
door as she drags her loneliness into
the light of happiness. She soars over
sounds of music as she jumps into a
pool of glass, getting power from the brain
of a broken arrow. She drifts back in
time, as she grabs at a snowflake
that floats like a feather through her
fingers. She fills the pools of sadness with
joy and makes flowers out of tumble-
weeds. Her return energizes my soul.

Betsy Neubauer :: Grade 5
Glen Lake Elementary School :: Hopkins

My Uncle Andy

The loud, noisy car, a piece of junk.
Enormous oil spots on his pants and shirt.
His two dogs, Tasha and Callie, barking and running stray.
Playing baseball with my brother and me.
His two children, Angie and Sara,
playing with my two sisters.
Wearing the same old dull hat every day.
Wearing his wire rim glasses, that four eyes.
Unlatching my hat whenever I wear it.
Opening our refrigerator and eating our junk food.
Boy, the times I had with him.

Mike Schmelzer :: Grade 5
Pullman Elementary School :: St. Paul Park

My Aunt

I like my aunt, she buys me lots of things for my birthday. She is very nice. One time when I was five years old, she bought me a go-cart and gave me some overalls. I like them.

She took me to the movies for the first time when I was three. When I was six, she bought me a 14 carat gold ring. She has a car and wears lots of gold. She is light skinned and she wears pretty Nikes. I love my aunt.

Her name is Trinar and she had a baby named Desmond. He died when he was five months old and that really bothers me. I loved him.

At his funeral my aunt and I cried to the end of the funeral. We still have him in our hearts.

She lives in Chicago, Illinois. She hates living there. Sometimes she comes to see me and she gives me money to get me and her a pop. We have fun together.

Darius Winfield :: Grade 4
Webster Magnet School :: St. Paul

I'M SORRY

Dear Grandma,

I know how much
you loved that pretty purple vase.
The one on your table.
How much did that pretty vase cost?

Tracy Morical :: Grade 4
Parker Elementary School :: Elk River

PORTRAIT OF GRANDPA

My grandpa was in World War II.
He came up to my house and visited
for a little bit. Then he went back to
Missouri and my Uncle Steve picked him
up at the airport and brought him to
McDonald's and he went to the bathroom
and had a heart attack. My uncle went in
to help him. He tried C.P.R. on him.
He brought him to the hospital and in
15 minutes he died. My Uncle Mark
contacted us. He told my mom
the whole story and then we went down
to Missouri to his funeral. I got
the flag that was on his casket.
Also got his dog tags. My grandpa
was big as a giant.

Eric Fox :: Grade 6
Cherokee Heights Elementary School :: St. Paul

FARMING

I help my grandpa every spring plant some things in his garden. The vegetable seeds seem like raindrops falling out of the sky. Then the leaves come out of the ground like a tornado picking up a hotel. The leaves feel as soft as the sky. By the time the vegetables are grown we pick the vegetables. They taste like the sugar we put on our cereal. My grandpa wears a blue hat almost beat, blue pants, brown belt with a jackknife in it, blue and white shirt, black shoes, hot face.

Kyle Wilkinson :: Grade 3
Buffalo Lake/Hector Elementary School :: Hector

GRANDPA

My Grandpa always talks.
It don't matter who—
my friends,
my brother's friends,
strangers—
it don't matter.
He smokes a pipe,
& the tobacco smells good.
He goes to the VFW,
but he never drinks.
He always wears a hat
that says, "God only
made a few perfect heads,
and the rest have hair."

Nic Malchow :: Grade 8
Rush City School :: Rush City

GRAMPS

Bye Gully, my gramps
says. Him and me in
the shop, with silent
tractors and buzzing
welder. I smell the
grain, oil and gas of
the old shop. Bye
Gully, my gramps
says. He has a draped
face and a funny
walk. The torch is
lying cold and still.
Bye Gully, my gramps
says. Me and him, him
and me. Bye Gully.

Randy Berger :: Grade 6
Badger Public Schools :: Badger

OLD RIPE BANANAS

The smell of old ripe
bananas
takes me back to the nursing home
my great-grandmother was in.
I remember walking in
seeing all the old people
clinging to my mother,
hoping we would go soon.
I remember hearing the
numbers of a bingo game
in the other room. When
we finally got to her room
I was so happy. My father
went to her side and started
yelling in her ear. She stared
at me and my sister. She offered
us some old ripe bananas, and then
some mints. We took the mints
always because the bananas
were such an old age.

Kristen Martin :: Grade 6
Long Prairie Elementary School :: Long Prairie

GRANDMOTHER

Grandmother sits alone in a chair,
Unable to walk or move any muscle in her small
body.
I ache for her.
She once would laugh and giggle with me,
The happiest woman I knew.
Now, I hear her crying at night,
The mournful cry of winter.
I stand outside her door,
Wishing she would call for me,
Wrap her arms around me.
But she doesn't,
She can't.
She cries for her husband who left her long ago;
she cries for her sons who have given up hope.
She used to put Band-Aids on the earth,
just her touch made the worst of pains
disappear.
I reach for her hand which now is frail,
I hold it close to my heart.
I'll never leave you Grandmother,
for that would mean leaving the memories
of your past vibrant red,
and only relying on the pale white that
replaced it.

Heather McNaught :: Grade 7
Blake Middle School :: Hopkins

GRANDPA'S HOUSE

When I go to my grandpa's house,
I thump up the stairs
to one of the rooms.
In each of the rooms
I have a fort.
I play a game
like chess
or make up songs.
It's not very dark,
but a little scary
in some places.
It's in a place
where nobody could ever
ever find it.
I wouldn't try
to find my fort, if I were you,
because you'd have to
find my grandpa's
house
first.

April Stave :: Grade 3
Roseau Elementary School :: Roseau

A year ago my grandparents moved into town from their farm. It was a pig farm. The barns were getting old. The wood was not as strong. All the paint was worn off and the roof was caving in. The chicken coop had burned down and the windows in the shed were all broken. Everyone liked the farm. It was a quiet, peaceful place for family and friends to meet and share their love and care for each other. It was a place for happy and sad feelings to be shared, stories and secrets to be told, rumors to be spread and a place to discuss problems. It was a place to cry and laugh, to welcome new family members and say goodbye to the old. It was a house of love, a place to feel love and to love others. Now it has all ended and we are starting over in a new house to have the same feeling in a different house. All we can do is to have memories of our old farm house that meant so much to us and hope for new memories in our town house. Where we can do the same things, have the same feelings, love others and feel loved.

Tessa Miller :: Grade 6
Buffalo Lake/Hector Middle School :: Buffalo Lake

No Snowflake is the Same and This One has Melted

My Mind is a Blank

My mind is a blank for things to write,
so on my pencil I do bite.

Karin Nelson :: Grade 5
Royal Oaks Elementary School :: Woodbury

Old Man with the Cans

As I look out
the window of our
car I see an old
man dressed warmly
with brown and white gloves
a stick across his back
with cans on each end

As I lose sight
of him the
thinking
begins

Oliver Ross :: Grade 4
Cherokee Heights Elementary School :: St. Paul

Parades are passing by and the people are eating. I'm lost. I saw my aunt in a car. I saw my uncle in his truck.

I was thinking to myself and said, "I can do what I want to do, say what I want to say, play like I want to play, eat what I want to eat, and dance like I want to dance."

That was how I spent the Cinco de Mayo of 1991.

Rudy Salinas :: Grade 5
Cherokee Heights Elementary School :: St. Paul

SANTA LUCIA DAY

It was a dark night. It wasn't really night out, but it felt like it was since it was getting so dark, so early. Everything was covered with a soft, white blanket of snow. It was Santa Lucia Day. Not everyone knew it though because only Swedish people celebrate it.

On Santa Lucia Day the oldest girl in the family gets up before dawn. She wakes up everyone in her family, serving them tea and biscuits on a wooden tray. She dresses in a long, white dress with a red sash. On her head she wears a wreath of lighted candles.

I was celebrating Santa Lucia Day but not in the same way. I was going to a church, not with my family like most people, but with my mom's friend Susan and her two children, Jamie and Jacob. It was a huge church but we were only using a small section of it. The light was dim, mostly lit with flaming candles. I had my doll with me, dressed exactly like Santa Lucia. Everyone thought she was wonderful, charming, and she was passed around from hand to hand, receiving many compliments.

Then soft music started, the doll was passed back, and Santa Lucia came down the aisle. She was followed by many others wearing white robes. She herself was dressed in the outfit I have told you about. Everyone was holding candles.

After it ended, everyone ate. There was lefse, a kind of very thin bread that you put butter and sugar on and roll it up. There were many kinds of cookies and other desserts, none of which looked familiar. When I finally left, it was very late and I was tired, but happy. Even though Santa Lucia Day is not a very common holiday, it is still a very special one.

Kirsten Feroe :: Grade 5
Cherokee Heights Elementary School :: St. Paul

Untitled

There I was, in the olive-green washtub
that on less happily weathered days
collected rainwater from the roof.
There I was,
naked to the sky and the crayola yellow sun
not ashamed of anything in my innocence.
I played in the cool water as ladybugs flitted about
and under the apple tree standing strong against the sky.
Laden with blossoms it stood like a mother
guarding me from wind and sun.
There we were, my washtub oasis and I;
bold against this great world that ended at the edge of the yard.
There I was,
ignorant of a war some thousands of miles away
where my brothers, my fellow men, were dying
ignorant and naive to cold hate and hot anger.
I was content knowing warm sun and cool water alone.
There I was,
the dove,
there I was
pure,
there, I was happy.

A. James Moore :: Grade 11
Caledonia High School :: Caledonia

FOR THE PRESENT

In Kindergarten one day
I was told to sit in a chair
"for the present."
So I sat and sat and sat,
and when all the kids
went out to play and
my teacher went out
to watch them
I still sat and sat and finally
my teacher came in
and asked me, "Why
don't you go out and play?"
So I said, "I'm waiting
for my present!"

Destin Anderson :: Grade 6
Central Middle School :: Columbia Heights

Eating Vegetables Takes Courage

When I eat green beans, lima beans and beets I feel like throwing up! They taste like the rubber on the bottom of a shoe and smell like yesterday's dirty socks. They even *feel* like the inside of a pumpkin. I try to throw them away, but I can't leave the table because I am not done eating. I stick them in my pocket and it takes courage to do that! Sometimes I forget to throw them away and it makes my pocket all dirty. Sometimes I wait until everybody leaves the table, and I make a run for it. Then I don't have to eat them vegies.

Mike Murphy :: Grade 6
Benjamin E. Mays Elementary School :: St. Paul

THE FASTEST RIDE EVER

As I looked up and saw my baby sister
sitting in the Johnny Jump-up,
(an interesting device used to help
young children learn to use their legs)
I remembered when I was younger
and used to have the most funnest time
in that thing. Yet, as I was watching her
jump in that wonderful toy,
she seemed to be using it all wrong.
I ran in the kitchen and took out
a medium-sized Tupperware bowl, then
ran back to where Amber was and gently
put the bowl on her head.
After that, I started to twist
the neat device around.
I really couldn't tell what Amber
was thinking inside her little head,
so I reassured her that this ride
was going to be fun! After I twisted
her around enough times,
I let that baby go
and watched her spin like a tornado.
Then she started to scream
like a fire truck.
What in the world could be wrong?
Soon my mom sent me to my room,
alone. I wasn't spoken to in a while.
What did I do wrong?

Sarah Paul :: Grade 5
Hillside Elementary School :: Cottage Grove

One day my mom took me to the Mall. We were looking for toys to donate to Toys for Tots. It was boring.

Right then something caught my eye. It was an ice cream cart. I just love ice cream!

When my mom wasn't looking, I went for it. When I got to the ice cream cart I remembered I didn't have any money so I went back to the store my mom was in. She wasn't there.

She must have gotten a different kid and it's a half hour drive home.

Oh no! I went to the store clerk and she described me on the loud speaker.

"Does anyone know Kelly Groon, blonde hair, blue eyes, red sweatshirt and blue jeans? If this little girl belongs to anyone, she will be in the Manager's office. Thank you."

So I guess I went to the Manager's office.

I introduced myself with tears in my eyes. I sat down in a big black chair. I sat and sat and sat for a half hour and still nobody showed up. By that time my cheeks were puffy from tears running down them.

I could smell a fresh cup of coffee and I could hear the Manager answering the phone. The big black chair I was sitting in felt comforting, very familiar like my mother's lap. That made me want to cry.

Every time the phone rang, I wished it was my mom. About the 15th time it rang, it was my mom. I was happy and I got to talk to her. She said she would be right down to pick me up and bring the other girl. She got back.

I wiped the tears out of my puffy eyes. I was happy, so happy. I jumped out of the big black chair and yelled,

"I'm happy!"

My mom got there, I ran over to her and gave her a great big bear hug and we went home.

A. J. Thomas :: Grade 3
Sandstone Elementary School :: Sandstone

THE DARKNESS OF NIGHT

I see the digits of my
clock moving 1:33 to 1:34. I see
car lights going down the street.
I hear my dog barking at flies.
I see fireflies shining. I can't
tell if they are inside or outside
because of the window that
I can't see. I now can see
my clock digits going from 2:01 to
2:02. I hear my dog barking
again at some crickets zooming
through the darkness of the night.
I hear my neighbor's dogs barking
at the cars roaming around
the street at 2:20. I see
the bathroom light turning on
as my mom walks in at 2:34. I see
it going off as my mom walks out.
She goes in her room. I see my
piano. I can imagine myself playing
"Morning Has Broken" at 4:01 to
4:02. I see myself asleep
dreaming I am rich.

Amanda Huber :: Grade 3
North Elementary School :: St. Peter

LUCKY

They call her Lucky
for she was.
When she was little
she became ill.
The doctors didn't know
what was next,
but she pulled through it
like a team of horses
pulling a buggy out of the mud.
Her only loss was that of not being able to hear
the birds chirping their tunes,
music flowing out of the radio,
her parents praising her like a saint
or accusing her like a mischievous cat.
She was lucky.
She can still talk
and sometimes remembers the sounds
she misses the most—
just the sound of her mother
telling her favorite bedtime story
or the rain pounding on the roof
like drums.

Christine Cirillo :: Grade 8
Oltman Junior High School :: St. Paul Park

THE EMPTY CHRISTMAS

The holiday season was definitely amongst the majority of us. One could virtually smell the evergreen trees and taste the sweet eggnog and sugary candy canes. Rounding each red and green corner, a different type of Saint Nicholas would appear, willing to hand out good wishes and accept generous tokens of any kind.

Quite a picturesque scene could be projected to the naked eye. But that day, I was offering my time to the local food shelf, to feed the homeless and spiritless.

Unclean and soft-spoken, people of all types trudged in from their cold, unkind streets. Generous presents and loving families were not a part of their holiday season.

Looking into each saddened and lonely pair of eyes that passed, a simple smile and my offering of time was all I could give. How I wished I could take each person home with me and fill them up with all the love and spirit they lacked.

This wish seemed an impossibility.

"Merry Christmas, Sir."

"Yah, I guess so."

Shannon Swanson :: Grade 11
Stillwater High School :: Stillwater

THE BOYS FROM WASIOJA*

In eighteen-hundred and sixty-one
The Civil War had just begun
Way out here, we heard the guns
Out in Wasioja

Chorus: Up on Seminary Hill
             You can see the pine trees still
             And the stories if you will
             (By) the boys of Wasioja

In eighteen-hundred and sixty-two
The wives and mothers and children too
Were worried about their men in blue
Out in Wasioja

(Chorus)

In eighteen-hundred and sixty-three
All the boys from Company "C"
They were down in Tennessee
Far from Wasioja

(Chorus)

In eighteen-hundred and sixty-four
Trees that weren't there before
(Were) planted for (the) boys lost in the war
All from Wasioja

(Chorus)

Ms. Haltvick's Class :: Grade 5
West Concord Elementary School :: West Concord

THAT DAY IN JUNE

The lights were flashing into my sleep-heavy eyes. From the daybed, situated near the door, I confusedly watched the paramedics jump out of the ambulance. There I sat, waiting, wondering what the hell was going on. A long-time friend and First Responder, Mary Johnson, led the small crew of people upstairs. About five minutes before, I'd received a call from Lori, my stepmother, telling me that she'd called for emergency help. Dad was having a very difficult time breathing and she was afraid, but I was assured that they would merely give him a few drugs and then be on their merry way.

So here they were. I waited for probably five minutes, but those moments stretched on. There were no feelings; no fear, sadness, or even knowledgeable resignation. I was undecided as to what I should have been doing, and my newly awakened condition rendered me vulnerable and unable to concentrate. I heard shuffles and bumps from upstairs, and people were running in and out of my house. Hidden in the shadows, I was able to hear snatches of conversation, ". . . know him? His name is Frank Morrell. He owns this place. I remember when my wife and I were first married, we came into the supper club to eat."

". . . look good. We're gonna have to move him fast."

And then Mary Johnson was at my side, telling me to get up and get dressed, that Lori and I would follow the ambulance to the hospital. Suddenly awake, my bones turned to red-hot ice. I flew out of bed and was ready in less than a minute. When Lori came down the stairs she was running, and her eyes blazed with a hard anger that was reflected in my own gaze. Children of Fear, we both understood well the untouched, scorching pain and uncertainty lying just beneath that capable veneer.

Together we jumped into the Lincoln, waiting for them to organize my father on the stretcher and pack him into the screaming, flashing, horrible monster that would transport him to the hospital. Lori kept telling me we had to be strong for him. Death is a series of rushing and waiting moments that alternately leave you functioning robot-like and thinking of what life will entail when it's all over. It makes the pragmatist pessimistic, and the idealist suicidally hopeful.

The stale scent of my father's Lincoln brought tears to my eyes, and at that point, halfway to the hospital in Willmar, I accepted that my father would die.

At the hospital, we were able to see him almost immediately. Lori and I both received our hugs and kisses before he promised himself, with tears in his eyes, that he was going to eat better, get that exercise we always dogged him about, and quit smoking. He went on and on, comparing himself to an old friend who had died of a heart attack for the same reasons. He was grateful for the second chance.

That night I stayed at my sister's home in Willmar. Alone on her living room floor, trying to sleep, I thought of the actual heart attack. He'd been crabby, unable to sleep, short of breath, and experiencing vertigo and pain in his arms. My father had been in the military for twenty-two years, during which and after, he'd owned and operated several small businesses. He didn't believe in pain or sickness, so when he became ill and spent spring opener (one of the busiest times of the year for the bar) in bed, I was badly frightened. I'd brought him aspirin and when I was sure I was out of his hearing range, I'd sobbed for almost an hour, while my boyfriend held my hand.

Finally on Monday, four days after the heart attack, he agreed to see a doctor. He was then diagnosed, severely reprimanded, and asked to stay "awhile." He'd been home for a few days and was having increasing difficulty breathing the night Lori and I trailed the paramedics to the hospital. Apparently his lungs had been slowly filling with fluid.

For three days after he was admitted for the fluid in his lungs, Lori and I visited faithfully, and learned that a part of his heart was dead and that, after he returned home, his activities would be limited. Just how limited, we weren't told.

During this stay in the hospital, impatient to get home, Dad was occasionally mischievous or rude to the nurses. He discovered that if he pulled the electrodes off his chest one by one, the nurse would come in and scold him. But, to his childish delight, if he removed them simultaneously, doctors and nurses would run to his room. He relayed all of his amusing capers to Bill (my step-brother who had returned home from Fort Richardson, Alaska only days before to help out at home); my boyfriend, Jeff; my friend, Maria; and myself two nights before he was to come home. He was jovial and planning his healthy future.

At home, Lori had been working my father's long hours to run the place, while worrying about him constantly. She was becoming run down, and on the day my father was to come home, she overslept. At eight o'clock, Dad called her, screaming about her not wanting him to come home and not caring.

"He was so angry. And then he dropped the phone."

That's all she could say through the tears on the way to the hospital. Then she apologized to me. I squeezed her hand, wiped away her tears, and said only, "I love you, and it's not your fault." My eyes were dry. I already knew, and I had to be strong for Lori.

In the hospital waiting room, Bill paced while Lori and I sat on the couch. She clutched me so tight I thought I would get hysterical, but I still did not cry. The doctor entered the room and introduced us to the chaplain, informed us that it did not look good, but he was trying, and left again. The chaplain was kind, but, absurdly, kept making small talk with me. Lori's hold on me tightened. When the doctor returned to Lori's expectant eyes, he said those dreaded, corny, movie-script words, "I'm sorry, Mrs. Morrell, there was nothing we could do."

She grabbed huge handfuls of her hair and began hysterically shouting, "No!" When it had died down to strangled gasps, Bill helped her into my father's death-room, and we all stood watching his gray, unlovely corpse. There was nothing alive or vibrant, and I feared that I would never remember him alive, only dead, on this dead bed. And neither image has faded. Somewhere along the line, I had acquired a can of Diet Pepsi and, under the circumstances, I became a bit hysterical. I was thinking that this was truly The World's Greatest Spectator Sport—move over tennis! I covered my mouth and giggled, but it was not a laugh. It was some kind of howl kept volumeless. Bill took it for crying until I explained, and then I asked to leave. The doctor said it was only coincidence that Dad and Lori were fighting when he died; it could have happened any time.

Lori stayed with the doctor for a few moments, while Bill and I went down the hall. There I lost it. He held me while I cried and sobbed. All the pain of the last few weeks came out, there in the hallway, in front of an old woman who kept asking, "Did someone die? What's going on?" He walked me to the car, told me I'd done very well, and that now I would take care of Lori as best I could and that there were always people to help.

I'd like to say that that morning, in the car, I came to grips with the age-old truth of life, and that now, not even the dark can scare me.

But I deal with it every day. And every day, that day in June seems a little farther away, until, eventually the only thing left will be those few memories and a vast emptiness so devoid of anything, I won't even know it's there.

Melody Morrell :: Grade 10
Elk River High School :: Elk River

UNTITLED

I was floating out in the sky, surrounded by blue and clouds. I came upon a door, it was made of wood with mouths stuck to it. They were talking and singing and yelling at the top of their lungs. The lips were big with red lipstick, their teeth were shiny white and their breath smelled like toothpaste. There was a key laying by the door, I touched it and I turned into air, invisible, but I could still see and touch myself. Suddenly I was sucked under the door through a little crack. It seemed like it took forever to get to the other side. When I finally got there, it was strange, but beautiful. There were a bunch of people, men, women and kids dressed in all white. They looked so peaceful and quiet. Could it be heaven?

Lori Kisrow :: Grade 8
Holy Name School :: Minneapolis

SWALLOWED

I was swallowed by my
picture . . .
I heard the strum of a
guitar as I slid down its
throat.
The belly of my picture was
black,
a splash of color here,
a glimpse of light over there.
Bones on the chairs. I
could tell that my picture
often swallowed people.
Scratches on the walls.
A door on the floor.
Barbed wire running up a
flag pole in the middle,
          The strum of a guitar.
     Black.
I was swallowed by my picture.

Theresa Ellefson :: Grade 7
Cleveland Middle School :: St. Paul

I loved pets,
but the only kind of pet I had were
Hamsters.
They kept dying and dying—
betcha I went through
eight hamsters in five years.
And every one that died
I buried in the back yard.
And every grave
I dropped a large rock on.
Once I wanted some hamsters back so
I got my little plastic shovel
and dug and dug—
But they were not there.
I kept putting more & more food
in their cages because I didn't know
why they were dying so fast.
Mom kept telling me, "If this one dies
it's the last one!" but
I cried so hard she bought more & more.
I have a bird now.
He's dead in a little box out in the garage
waiting for Spring so I can bury him
and drop a big rock on the grave.

Chris Robinson :: Grade 8
Central Middle School :: Columbia Heights

The Days of Childhood

Back to the age of playing with Troy, Rick and Trenton,
Back to the age of playing camping
The years of Quarry Hill bike rides
of being afraid of the dark
and fearing that someone would shoot
me in my sleep, wearing five
thick blankets to protect me
Back to the age of putting balloons
on bikes to have motorcycles
Back to the age of being afraid
of "Unsolved Mysteries" on TV
Back to the age of playing
in the woods of Quarry Hill
Back to the age of reading
in an empty closet
No snowflake is the same
and this one has melted.

Mark Anderson :: Grade 5
Hoover Elementary School :: Rochester

After World War II he returned home, home where the grass was still green, where the air and the water were still clean. He told me that was when he realized he was going to start dancing in Pow-wows.

"The beat of the drums and the singing is all linked together as in a story about the old legends, animals, warriors and ancient places. When you dance, your feet move in a motion of two beats to a foot and you feel a warmth inside yourself," he told me one day when he was talking about the old days. His outfit is very beautiful. It has a lot of beadwork in the shape of flowers in traditional Ojibway fashion. He is a grass dancer, still dancing to this day.

Gerald Hawk :: Grade 11
Warroad High School :: Warroad

He Was Just Showing Him Where the Green Grass Was

If You Listen

If you listen
hard enough,
you will hear
the secrets of the world
in the whisper of the wind.

Jenny Brooke Nannenga :: Grade 7
Oltman Junior High School :: St. Paul Park

THE POND

My favorite place in the world—the simple pond behind the barn. You can't see it but it isn't that far away.

I go there about three times a week. It's quiet and it's fun to have a place to run and carve in the wood.

There are many trees around the pond. There are places to climb and run. But my favorite is on the hill. There is a tree there and I can see the lake from way up there.

It is the best in the world to me.

Sam St. Marie :: Grade 5
Holy Family School :: Albany

THE LAKE

The dock supporting us is worn smooth
And shiny
From paws
And feet
Passing over it time after time.

The air resting gently on our backs
is dark
And moist.

The water rising and falling
Over our bare feet
Nips quietly at the shoreline.

Bats rush overhead,
Not missing a thing in their blindness
and chasing away our only enemies
On The Lake.

Kristina Spaulding :: Grade 9
Stillwater Junior High School :: Stillwater

BLACK DOG'S TRAIL*

Back in 1854
From the Minnesota River's shore
There was a path called Black Dog's Trail
From the Mdewakaton
Upon this trail they did walk
Upon this trail they did stalk
They lived their lives so free on Black Dog's Trail
Mdewakaton, Mdewakaton, Mdewakaton, Black Dog's Trail

In 1855
Lebanon township was alive
On the Mendota Big Sioux River Road
Black Dog's Trail
Upon this trail they did ride
Upon this trail they took pride
They lived their lives so differently on Black Dog's Trail
Mdewakaton, Mdewakaton, Mdewakaton, Black Dog's Trail

In 1856
Once again they had a road to fix
Made it long they made it wide
Black Dog's Trail
Upon this road they changed the name
Upon this road more people came
And now today it's called Dodd Road, Black Dog's Trail
Mdewakaton, Mdewakaton, Mdewakaton, Black Dog's Trail
Mdewakaton, Mdewakaton, Mdewakaton, Black Dog's Trail

Ms. Roble's Class :: Grade 4
Westview Elementary School :: Rosemount

UNTITLED

Every time I smell fresh grass
    clippings I think of the
    house next door . . .
Its old, dirty white frame slowly
    sinking in . . .
Its long, unclipped grass and weeds
    continuing on with life . . .
The crickets and grasshoppers
    leaping this way, that way . . .
Its vacant yard home to
    small, brown squirrels . . .
    The old rickety screen door tossing
    in the hollow, moaning wind . . .
But then the mower comes to
    execute the grass,
    and the weeds only settle
    in the woods just beyond . . .

Sara DeRosier :: Grade 5
McGregor School :: McGregor

UNTITLED

In the garden
    there was a rose
so small and pale and pink.
On the rose
    there was dew,
a drop of starlight
    on the rose.
When this dew was not this dew,
was it starlight?
Starlight on a wave
    in the sea
shimmering, shining starlight.
Was this dew
      a drop
    of starlight?
A drop, a drip, a cloud's
    teardrop,
a star on the rose,
small pink rose
In the garden.

Nina Weberg :: Grade 6
Twin Bluff Middle School :: Red Wing

RAIN IN THE NIGHT

Rain in the night
you call to me from
hot summer skies
whispering cool thoughts
of blue as I lie
sweaty in a bed of steam.
I love nothing so much as
rain in the night, falling
to the rhythm of the mind
where dreams are real
and fantasy is forever
as I float in sleep.
Rain in the night
don't let me be the black
of the dead, because I am
the Gypsy girl who was swaying
on the surface of the pool.
Don't let them drag me under
to the decaying bodies of creatures
once alive.
Rain in the night
I want to stand beneath you
so you will wash away
the tape that hangs on its memories
making them too cloudy for me
to see through.
Rain in the night
where do you hide your wings?
Whom do you seek?

Teresa March :: Grade 11
Long Prairie High School :: Long Prairie

Snow

Snow is tired of being pushed around by wind.
It hates being melted by the sun.
Snow is so mad it wants to make a blizzard.
It slashes my cheeks like rocks,
It falls in large piles the wind can't blow over.

Snow loves to parachute off the clouds.
It loves to close schools,
Snow loves to trap cars in driveways
Or make them collide.

Snow turns itself into hail to get back at kids who eat snow.
It becomes a friend who lets me build a snow fort.
It turns my house into a white palace.
Snow likes kids who play inside it,
Loves the feel of sled runners racing through the drifts.
Snow likes to look delicate but it is heavy when I shovel it.
It hates being stabbed by shovels that feel like a fork in its back.

I like to walk in the snow.
It crunches like fortune cookies under my feet.
I like picking it up and forming a solid snowball to throw.
Snow hates getting caught in my shoes 'cause it melts when I walk
    inside.
It hates how the plow undresses the streets.
It hates watching its white coat get dirtied by salt.
Snow retreats into a cave and spends eons planning just when and
    where to fall.
It always comes a month before winter.
It pores over ancient charts and complex maps
And falls on everyone else's school but ours
Just to spite us.

Snow dreams of turning the weatherman's radar into snow
To make him look stupid.
It likes to trick humans by ruining our plans.
It obscures ice patches so we'll slip and fall.
It likes to trip Olympic skiers.

Snow tries to trick groundhog into seeing his shadow.
It drives little animals back into their homes.
It likes to ride on dogs.

Snow dreams of flying to Hawaii to cover up volcanos and pineapples.
It flees when the temperature is above freezing
But it hates to leave.
It is always busy.
It hates to see people vacation in Florida.

Snow thinks tropical tribes should be jealous.
Snow dreams of being crowned king at the Winter Carnival.
It dreams of going home to White Earth Reservation
To hibernate for the summer.

Mr. Prokasky's Class :: Grade 5
Crestview Elementary School :: Cottage Grove

THE RHINOCEROS AND THE ELEPHANT

The rhinoceros is stomping
through the green grass.
It is chasing an elephant.

Boom Boom Boom Boom Boom!
He was just showing him
where the green grass was.

Christopher Audette :: Grade 1
Aquila Primary Center :: St. Louis Park

SHEEP

Oh, sheep,
oh, clothier of men,
warmer of life.
Beast of shelter from gloomy days,
cold rainy hours,
blustery, chafing winds.

A money bin
waiting to be shed
of heavy layers of endless death.
Only to be
chopped
pushed
squeezed
and punished
until the ransacking unforgiving blade cuts off
layers of whipped cream
to reveal their lifelong shame and sorrow.

A shell-less pink turtle stands there.

The sheep shearer with his electrical toy of torture
cannot be fazed
by the humiliation of the gentle creature.
He laughs
at the taste of blood and sweat
tingling on his lips.

The sheep crouches in the shadow of fear,
scrambling unconsciously
away from the Satan of shearers.
Light beams
onto the naked corpse
lying slumped over dead.
But will awaken

from his slumber.
His will to live blooms
on his hair of life.

Mike Hanslick :: Grade 8
GFW Middle School :: Fairfax

THE WORLD OF WHALES

We are the great gentle family of whales.

Though we belong to two clans, we still live together in peace and
    harmony
In our ocean world.

We are the graceful water-ballet dancers.

I am BELUGA. I chirp like a canary.
I am MINKE. Find me in all the oceans.
I am RIVER DOLPHIN from the Ganges.
I am SEI. I live with my brother in all the oceans.
I am NARWAHL, unicorn of the sea.
I am RIGHT. You almost lost me.
I am PORPOISE. Smart and talented.
I am BOWHEAD, a gift of life to the Earth-people.
I am GRAY, like the color of shadows in the moonlight.
I am PILOT, who follows the leader.
I am FINBACK, gentle giant of the sea.
I am ORCA, fierce warrior of the deep.
I am HUMPBACK, the upside down opera singer.
I am DOLPHIN, the clown of your circus.
I am SPERM WHALE. Remember Moby Dick?
I am BOTTLENOSE. Like all elders I gray with age.
I am the BLUE leviathan of the waves.
I am BEAKED, a bird of the blue waters.
I am BRYDE'S. I honeymoon in the tropics.

We are the whales, the gentle monarchs of the earth's oceans.

We have feelings too.
Hear our voices speaking out "Endangered, endangered, endangered."

Help us survive on Mother Earth.

Ms. Rupert's Class :: Grade 8
Central Middle School :: Columbia Heights

Old Three Legs*

Come gather around, hear our story
A story strange but true
Of the killin' wolf called "Three Legs"
I'll sing of him to you, I'll sing of him to you

The Indians called him "Spirit Wolf"
He was fierce and strong
They chased him once for 13 days
For him that wasn't long, for him that wasn't long

"Old Three Legs" was a killer
A "Terrorizer" to be exact
He'd run from country to country
Now what to you think about that? Now what do you think about
    that?

There once was a man you see
Grover Amundson went insane
Because of that "Old Three Legs"
I told it nice and plain, I told it nice and plain

Farmers were so terrified,
They tied a lamb to a tree
Then "Old Three Legs" came around
He said "They're trying to get me, they're trying to get me"

Three days later they found the trap
But the "Spirit Wolf" was not around
All he left behind him was a single paw on the ground
A single paw on the ground

Then one day two hunters came
And tried to shoot him down
but the bullets did not hit him
They just went around, they just went around

As age crept up on "Three Legs"
He lost his lightning speed
But the killing power of his jaws
Remained part of his creed, remained part of his creed

Then Fred Darkow came to the country
After "Three Legs" he did go
The most famous wolf of all
Lay dead in the snow, lay dead in the snow

Mr. Sprafka's Class :: Grade 5
Rossman Elementary School :: Detroit Lakes

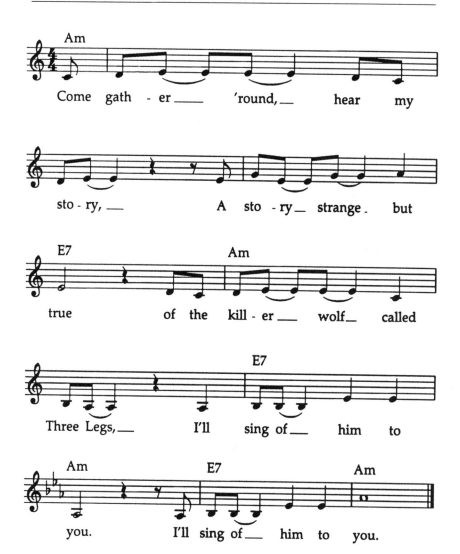

The Bobcat

Your breathtaking leap
out of the fire is your birth.

At night
you stare at the
shadowy moon
tumbling across the
sky.
You stare at him,
green with envy,
wishing you too
could fly.

You rush through the crisp, green
grass.
You skim through the water,
clear as glass.

Your claws, like daggers
ripping rough leather.
The slits in your eyes
like fire
set off by dangerous weather.

You are the spirit
that flies
through the mountains
at night.

Your growl is the person's
low cry of
excruciating pain.

You are as young
as the newly
brightened day;
as young as
spring leaf buds
that tremble and sway.

Your hunger as fierce
as a charging pack of bulls.

Your speed, your grace,
the beauty of color engraved in
your face.

You see lightning above you,
but you are not scared,
for you have great courage.

You are thunder
that crashes over the sea.

You will stay in the woods
forever, to be
ruler of the
        forest.

Angela May :: Grade 5
Tanglen Elementary School :: Hopkins

When wind met flames
the Hyena was created
by the powers
of God.

The Hyena's hunger
is as dark
as a nightmare.

Hyena is as
ancient as
Greek mythology.

Hyena's power makes
the Dead Sea die of mercy.

Hyena is the spirit
that gives
strength to all people.

Adam Bahr :: Grade 3
Pinecrest Elementary School :: Hastings

HURRICANE'S ENVY

It was the hunt of the ferret.

The immense sky,
Easily devouring the snowy moon
Which rolls to its death at dawn,
As the plump rodent walks
Toward the ferret's ambush
Of death and celebration.

In the gentle of morning,
Broken by the ferocity of a tornado,
A ferret was brought forth
Of sun-bleached earth.

The ferret, as young
as a flash of lightning preceding thunder,
But as old and wise as a sea turtle
Burying her eggs on a beach.

The ferret is a snake
Flying on the legs of deer.
His claws a surgeon's scalpel,
Cutting to the soul of his prey.
With eyes like a starless, midnight sky,
He hunts in the homes of his quarry.
His tail is a tree
Needed to warm his nose.

With hunger, furious
As a midsummer thunderstorm,
Ferret streaks through emerald forests.
The thrill of chasing larger prey
Pounding in strained muscles.
The rabbit slows.
A leap from the ferret and a flash of teeth,

And the rabbit lies still
On brown earth, turning red.

The silence of the ferret
Is the wind knocking grass together.
Ferret's gentleness, so great
that mirrored lakes look gnarled,
But its ferocity is a hurricane's envy.

Ferret is the stalker
Hunting all challengers of his majesty.

Jacob Woldstad :: Grade 9
Swanville Public Schools :: Swanville

Dragon Song

In the dragon's flight
The eagle withers with jealousy.
Burning a golden path through the night sky;
Flaming in his splendor, glorious.

The memory of lightning, dragon is,
Vague, yet permanently imprinted on the passerby's mind.

Dragon, as old as the mountain's silence
While as young as the spring rains.

When a dragon is conceived,
The unimportant shell bursts.
Infinite in imperishable glory,
The dragon is brought forth.

His claws are as sharp as swords,
Sheathed, as soft as a kitten.
His fiery breath,
Hotter than a furnace.
His wings, as his life,
Are as long as a millennium in both space and time.
His scales, a hard but beautiful rainbow of colors.
His body, as large and tough as the tallest oak.

The dragon's silence is as stealthy as lava,
Slowly seeping through fathoms of rock.
His wings churning the air like a tornado.

His hunger, as corroding as the passage of time.

The frozen moon, silent sentinel of the night sky
Idly watching him circle the earth.
The crystal waterfall, locked in solemn beauty,
Noisely paying him homage,
The last golden leaves slowly drifting to the ground,

Colorfully saluting him.
It was the splendor of the dragon.

David Lonning :: Grade 5
Alice Smith Elementary School :: Hopkins

THE MAN IN THE MOON

There was a rich man and it was Halloween. Everyone dressed in a costume, but there was a man in a monster suit. The rich man said, "I want the moon to hang in my room!" So the man in the monster suit said, "I'll do it." So the man built a tower so tall that it took him a year. Then the rich man said, "Climb it now!!" So he did. It took the man in the monster suit a whole year to climb it. When he reached the top, he jumped and his hand caught the moon and he climbed into it. And he said, "I will stay here and not with the rich man," and he never came back.

Ben Rosenthal :: Grade 2
Webster Magnet School :: St. Paul

(Based upon the comments of third and fourth graders who were planting trees, who were asked what they wished for the trees they put in the ground.)

Lord, I humbly come to you today to ask a favor for a friend. The journey he must face is long and frightening. He feels so alone. He doesn't know if he can continue. But Lord, he must because he is needed very, very dearly. He will give the earth life. He will give us moisture and shelter. He will give us comfort when we need a friend to talk to and protection when we are scared. He will give animals a sturdy home in which to raise a strong healthy family. His soothing lullabies will sing me to sleep on stormy eves. He will give us fresh, clean air to breathe.

Lord, please help this little tree to grow up safe and strong. Let his branches calm a saddened child's crying. Let his wide, brown trunk bear the marks of first loves forever. Let his loving branches embrace many storms with open arms and let them dance in happiness. Let his graceful leaflets climb and climb until they brush the sky. Let the deep colors of a bluebird and the busy brown face of a squirrel find shelter among his loving branches. But most importantly, Lord Jesus, let a wondrous child find a special friend in this little tree. May they grow and grow together and live forever in immortality.

Please help this tree on his journey, Lord Jesus. This little tree will give us our life if you will just give him his. Amen.

Clint Smith :: Grade 10
Lanesboro High School :: Lanesboro

In the Temple
Black as Night
Buddha
With a Ruby and Jade Tiger
Glowing to Bring Light.
The Tiger so Soft
But yet Very Hard
Body of Mythical Gold
Heart of Scintillating Red
Eyes of Glossy Green
Surrounded by Everything
Though Nothing is There.

Lauren Ashley Borgen :: Grade 5
Norman County West Schools :: Hendrum

Praise to the fragrance of a fresh-cut rose
    For it gives you the courage to break away.
    Petal by petal,
    You become your own.

Praise to the smell of a new-fallen rain
    For it makes your soul alive and renewed.
    Drop by Drop
    You shine like the sun.

Praise to the scent of a breezy Fall day
    For its inviting coolness captures a warmth.
    Leaf by leaf
    You die into growth.

Sara Mess :: Grade 11
Battle Lake High School :: Battle Lake

Love
        Laughs through the heart,
Anger
        Barks through the tongue,
Sadness
        Whispers through the ears,
Touch
        Slides through the veins,
Boredom
        Humphs through the nose,
Jealousy
        Grabs at the throat,
Hurt
        Wanders through the head,
Horror
        Ponders at the brain cell.

Anne Miller :: Grade 4
Richfield Intermediate School :: Richfield

THE DARKNESS INSIDE

If I sit inside the dark,
the darkness is inside of me.
It swirls inside like a flood
of fluttering butterflies.
The darkness soothes me.
I feel relaxed, but a part of
me dances and leaps for joy.
It sings and hums.
I am truly happy.
The darkness seeps through
my skin.
I can feel the stillness
being poured inside,
building up
until I explode with happiness.
If I sit inside the dark,
the darkness is inside of me.
It swirls inside
like a flood of butterflies
and I am happy.

Kelly Ridge :: Grade 5
Maternity of Mary / St. Andrew School :: St. Paul

I once walked on fleece,
colored silken petals
that fall from the pale moonlight
in the velvet sky.
Falling by the baby blue lake.

I once was a queen in Sathrine.
Some say I was a dreamer,
but I don't believe that,
I believe I was really there.

It was Hamlet who said,
"To be or not to be,
that is the question."

I will answer it.

To be, is to live.
Not to be, is to live sadly.
So try to live your way
and never look back.
But think about what is to come.
Maybe it will be the end of life
or the beginning of a
new life.

As people,
we can't be explained,
just enriched with joy
we are alive.

Susy Henninger :: Grade 6
Barnum Elementary School :: Barnum

I sing the song of the
mourning dove, I whisper the words
of the sea gull.

I run on the beach
with a shell in my hand,
I dance in the night
until the morning ruins
the darkness.

The ocean and the land
should always be equal,
as long as they can survive.

As I am blinded
by the sun's beauty,
I gaze out at
the sea's waves,
and I discover
that it is just a
pool of tears.

I am as old as
the sun's glory,
yet as young as
the rain that
falls into the sea.

It is dusk and I am
lying on the beach
while sea gulls flutter
and squawk around my head,
and while the sun is slowly
getting ready for bed.

I will follow you to the
  end of the rainbow,
where the fortune is
      never-ending.

The mist of lonely rain
    falls silently to my feet,
and turns to words.

The hushed sound
  of the waves
is my life, my soul.

Kate Griep :: Grade 5
Katherine Curren Elementary School :: Hopkins

O FLAME

O flame, you are
a flame that we roast
marshmallows for
marshmallow-grams.
We sing songs around you.

O flame sometimes
you do bad things
to earth. You staticly
move about a forest with
other flames as if you
are driving a race car
for fun.

O flame, you can
be beautiful, you
can dress up in
red, yellow and
orange, and dance
as if you are a
ballerina.

O flame, you can
look like evil
things. You can
look like an
evil witch's hat and
broom.

O flame I love
to climb your
cliffs and mountains
in my heart.

O flame, you keep
me going, and
at night you
stop burning and
I stop burning with
you.

Anna Warnes :: Grade 3
Aquila Primary Center :: St. Louis Park

MONDAY

The clock is like a cheetah running
as fast as it can. The tick tock
taste is a drowning person.
The sound is silent as a pig and as
loud as a mouse. It smells like
a meal that is prepared in 30 minutes.
It is the beginning and end of the time
zone. One clock lives for everyone
but two clocks live for the young. The
clock is like a deformed baby: 3 hands
and no arms. Clocks can only
count to twelve. The clock is like
the universe, planets keep going around
and around the year. It is the four
corners of time, tick tock, tick
tock, tick, tick.

Matt Marvin :: Grade 6
Pullman Elementary School :: St. Paul Park

A Day Before Me

A girl with long pencil scratches for hair
stands off in the corner,
rectangular suitcase in hand.

In the center of the paper,
stand children, five
in a straight line.
Their circular heads rise,
one higher than the others.

The far side of the paper holds another
two figures, a man and a woman.
They look connected by the arms
but are really only holding hands.

The girl in the corner frowns,
she belongs with the others.
The children are crying pencil-mark tears.
They are too young to understand.

A line goes from cheek to cheek
on the woman and man.
Their faces hold no expression.

Jessica Williams :: Grade 8
Richfield Junior High School :: Richfield

Scene: A cave. At the opening is a huge fire, played by three people who wave their arms in a fire-like motion. Inside the cave is an OLD MAN whose skin is emerald green. In fact, on closer inspection we see that he has turned into an emerald. He rocks in a rocking chair and sings to himself. A drum, three flutes and two violins provide underscoring for his song:

OLD MAN
My cave is beautiful and dark
My cave is beautiful and dark
My cave is beautiful and dark

Boy am I singing now!

My cave is beautiful and dark
My cave is beautiful and dark
My cave is beautiful and dark

I wish I had some light.

> (Music stops.
> He gets up. With stiffness and pain, walks to the cave opening. He tries to go out into the daylight. His eyes are seared by the light. Clarinets and trumpets blast ugly notes to sound his agony. He withdraws, covering his eyes. He stumbles back into the chair, and begins to rock and sing again. Music under:)

My cave is beautiful and dark
My cave is beautiful and dark
My cave is beautiful and dark

Boy am I singing now!

My cave is beautiful and dark
My cave is beautiful and dark
My cave is beautiful and dark

I wish I had some light.

(A BOY enters the cave, exploring. The OLD MAN sees him, shouts:)

OLD MAN

Who goes there?

BOY

Me.

OLD MAN

(Gets up, jumps up and down.)
Get out!! Get out, and never come back! Get out!!

(The BOY runs out, but hides and watches as the OLD MAN returns to his chair and sings.)

My cave is beautiful and dark
My cave is beautiful and dark
My cave is beautiful and dark

Boy am I singing now!

My cave is beautiful and dark
My cave is beautiful and dark

(The OLD MAN begins to cramp up, all over his body. In twisted agony, he falls out of the chair and onto the floor, motionless. The BOY enters the cave, and goes carefully to the OLD MAN. The BOY reaches slowly out, touches the OLD MAN. Sudden drum strike, and a guitar string pluck. The BOY jumps back, his hand, cramped and twisted.)

BOY

My hand. It's turned into an emerald?

(Music starts again, hypnotic. The BOY stumbles backwards into the rocking chair. He rocks, and begins to sing, like the old man.)

My cave is beautiful and dark
My cave is beautiful and dark
My cave is beautiful and dark

Boy am I singing now!

My cave is beautiful and dark

> (He suddenly jumps out of the chair, looks at it as though it has
> some power over him.
>
> Music again, but slightly different sound, as though it was the
> boy's own music. Five people enter from deeper in the cave.
> They walk in time to the music, carrying a rocking chair. They set
> the chair down. Two go to block the entrance to the cave. One
> motions for the BOY to sit in the new chair.)

>   PERSON

Would you like to have a seat?

>   BOY

> (Backing away)

No.

> (The other two people go to the BOY, take him to the chair,
> push him into it. The BOY begins to sing:)

My cave is beautiful and dark
My cave is beautiful and dark
My cave is beautiful and dark

Boy am I singing now!

My cave is beautiful and dark

> (He tries to get out of the chair. They push him back into it.)

My cave is beautiful and dark
My cave is beautiful and dark
My cave is beautiful and dark

(He tries to get out. They push him back into the chair.)

My cave is beautiful and dark
My cave is beautiful and dark

I wish I had some light.

My cave is beautiful and dark
My cave is beautiful and dark
My cave is beautiful and dark

Boy am I singing now!

> (As the BOY sings, the five people pick up the OLD MAN and his chair, and carry him deep into the cave. The BOY continues singing.)

My cave is beautiful and dark
My cave is beautiful and dark
My cave is beautiful and dark

I wish I had some light.

> (The BOY goes to the entrance of the cave, withdraws in agony at the light, stumbles back into his chair. He continues his song, and the play fades out.)

Ms. Larson's Class :: Grade 5
Middleton Elementary School :: Woodbury

UNTITLED

Once upon a time there was a god named Goma. He had two sons, Cool and Whip. Goma packed his elephants with water and gold dust and sent his two sons into the west to find where the three skies of air met.

They walked quickly for many days and nights until they reached the lakes of life and fire.

Cool crossed the lakes of life and fire by walking on the power of truth.

Whip crossed the lakes of life and fire on air and gold dust.

As they crossed the bridge their bodies disappeared, captured by the power of the bridge. But their spirits remained. Their spirits captured the tiger of loyalty who convinced the bridge of power to give their bodies back to Cool and Whip.

The tiger then made the boys kings of the land, where they ruled until they were turned into a red elephant.

One day the red elephant fell into the water of the lake of life and fire and turned into a courageous hunter. The hunter captured a dog and then went to a church to pray. The church was grateful to the hunter for his prayers and turned him back into an elephant and the elephant back into Cool and Whip.

The boys continued their journey. At last they found where the three skies met. Overcome by the sight, Whip died and Cool returned to his father with the good news of finding the three skies and the bad news of Whip's death.

Mike Timmerman and Derrick Joens :: Grade 7
Worthington Junior High School :: Worthington

OH ROSE, HOW I HATE YOU

Oh, rose, how like true life you really are.
So beautiful at times, with sadness
right behind the other petal,
knowing you won't last forever.
You'll die, beautiful rose,
and you'll fall to a crisp darkness
to be forgotten forever.

Each person is sent from above
on a mission; we serve our purpose,
some of us to make the world beautiful,
others to darken the days of others.
Once we are done with our deed,
we fall to the ground and melt away,
to be forgotten forever by those to come.

Today is a day of emptiness and sorrow.
I look back on other years
and wonder why I've become what I am.
Each day has been like a painting for me.

The thorns prick you when you least
expect it, as life pricks you even harder.

Maybe then, those sharp pricks
on your stem won't hurt others.
Maybe then your beauty won't disguise
your nastiness.

Amy Larson :: Grade 12
Prior Lake High School :: Prior Lake

UNTITLED

A moonbeam got lost in my room last night.
I couldn't save it.
I couldn't find its way to where it belonged.
It dwindled and died at my fingertips. . . .

Lost in my room, pale silver,
whispering incomprehensible doubts.
Floating among white sheets and grey,
My sleep was unstirred.
   I dreamed of sweet lips and soft hands.

If I'd opened my eyes, it would have found
its place, to be my waking dreams, to shine
from behind my eyes.
As my dream ended, the lips that kissed, the
ivory hands turned cold to stone and I awoke
kissing salt.
   I was too late. I couldn't hold on to
what was left. . . .
   Now a shadow lurks where the moon
should have been.

Heather Carroll :: Grade 11
Roseville High School :: Roseville

GUITAR

A sleek machine of speed
Shredding power
Guitar
Your curves entice me
Your neck chaffs my fingers
Like sub-zero wind
Up and down
Your neck I speed
Until my fingers bleed, bleed
Blood red fire.

Jay Pleban :: Grade 10
Mahtomedi High School :: Mahtomedi

THE TRUTH OF A PENCIL

A lonely pencil waiting to be warmed up,
waiting to be used. Words
want to come out but can't. The fire's
burning inside, a little light shining
like a sun rising. It's like a rocket
wanting to go into space, but can't.
It's a blizzard of words.

Gina Baglio :: Grade 5
St. Rose of Lima School :: Roseville

ALICE

Smell the cake in the oven,
see your mother kneading the dough
madly; she is the Red Queen
cooking her tarts.

A curious thought. . . .

You venture farther,
knowing there is a link
between Alice and your own name.

Going to school is like
falling down the rabbit-hole,
chasing education as if it
were the white rabbit.

The teacher is the Walrus,
slurping up egos and pride,
like baby oysters.
Your temper and big mouth
are the only oysters left behind.

Your friends are so like
Tweedledum and Tweedledee,
rattling their inane problems,
never really hearing you at all.

Father is the Jabberwocky,
a fearsome creature
devouring dreams and fantasy
like kernels of buttered popcorn.

Your brother is the carpenter,
so slow, maddening, stupid,
making you wild with frustration.

How real fantasy is,
how true imagination,
how like Alice you are,
caught, trapped in a fairy tale
more real than truth. . . .

Alison Crosby :: Grade 8
McGregor Schools :: McGregor

If You Praise a Word, It Turns Into a Poem

Praise to this poem
    for letting me write it,
To book titles
    that give away clues.

Praise to the time on a watch
    so I am not late,
To the shell
    that washes up on shore for me.

Praise to the fly's eye
    with which he sees everything.
To the grass
    that whistles when I blow it.

Praise to the mud
    that makes me dirty when I play,
To the thunder
    that warns me of a lightning flash.

Praise to my name
    without which I'd be no one,
To this poem
    for letting me write it.

Caitlin Weber :: Grade 4
Christa McAuliffe Elementary School :: Hastings

AUTHOR INDEX

School Index

Program Writers 1991–1992

Sigrid Bergie
John Caddy
Florence Chard Dacey
Margot Fortunato Galt
Billy Golfus
Dana Jensen
Syl Jones
Gita Kar
Charlie Maguire
Roy McBride
Ken Meter
Jaime Meyer
John Minczeski
Beverly Acuff Momoi
Jim Northrup, Jr.
Sheila O'Connor
Joe Paddock
Nancy Paddock
Ruth Roston
Richard Solly
Deborah Stein
Roberta Hill Whiteman